Brown Hares
in the
Derbyshire Dales

One of the declared aims of the United Kingdom Biodiversity Action Plan was to 'Use the popularity of brown hares to highlight the impact on biodiversity of modern agricultural practices and loss of mixed farms'.

This book attempts in a small way to do just that.

Published by Lepusbook 2010

Text and photographs © Christine Gregory 2010

Design Caroline Firenza

Printed by northend creative print solutions

ISBN 978-0-901100-92-4

NATIONAL PARK AUTHORITY

Supported by the Sustainable Development Fund

This book was produced with funding from the
Peak District National Park Authority
Sustainable Development Fund.

The ideas and views expressed in this book are those of the author and do not necessarily reflect the
policies or aims of the Peak District National Park Authority or of the Derbyshire Wildlife Trust

Brown Hares
in the
Derbyshire Dales

Words and photographs by Christine Gregory

Contents

Foreword

This book on the brown hare in the Derbyshire Dales is a marvellous testament to Christine Gregory's love of nature and the landscape where she lives. The book, richly illustrated with beautiful photographs, provides a rare insight into the hare as an increasingly endangered species; and also the myths and legends surrounding these mysterious and solitary animals.

To me the broader and more fundamental purpose of this book, however, is to propose the hare as an indicator species for the good management of land and the fragile ecosystem which we as humans are guardians of.

This study of the hare in the relatively protected environment of the Peak District National Park will help to provide inspiration to enable the hare, a more ancient species than humans, to thrive together with us into the distant future.

Lord Edward Manners
Haddon Hall, Derbyshire
September 2010

Introduction

2010 is the United Nations International Year of Biodiversity.

The accelerating extinction of many species around the world was recognised at the Earth Summit in Rio in 1993. There was growing understanding that species are interdependent and that the breakdown of the complex web of life by man's activities on the earth ultimately threatens us all

Nations that signed the Convention on Biodiversity went on to draw up Biodiversity Action Plans (BAPS) for the most threatened species.

The brown hare (Lepus europaeus) was one of the first species chosen by the UK government. The target was to double its population by the year 2010.

The brown hare was chosen not because it is especially rare or in danger of extinction, but because the hare, once a common creature of British farmland, had become scarcer and entirely absent in some areas. There has been an estimated 75% decline in the population since the war.

The term biodiversity refers to the variety of life forms within an ecosystem. The hare is part of a community of mammals, birds, insects, plants and other organisms that share a farmland habitat. Modern agricultural methods have fundamentally altered not only the look of the countryside but also what can live in it, thus diminishing its biodiversity.

The beautiful landscape of the Derbyshire Dales is hare country.

I have spent many hours over the last two years watching, following and photographing brown hares close to my home in Youlgrave. Like so many people, I am captivated by their beauty, speed and mystery. I wanted to see more of how they live their often solitary and tough lives out in the open from birth. I have seen them scratch through deep snow to reach frozen grass, cavort madly through spring and summer fields or rest up peacefully on a hillside.

Last year I became aware of the aims of Britain's Biodiversity Action Plan with regard to the hare. I had already made the link between places where hares appeared to thrive and the richness of habitat in terms of bird, insect and plant species.

I had an opportunity to produce this book with a grant from the Peak District National Park Authority Sustainable Development Fund. I hope to engage wider interest in the fragile presence of hares in the pastures of the Derbyshire Dales and to draw attention to the changes in farming practice that have caused the collapse in populations of hares and ground nesting birds including the skylark, lapwing, grey partridge and curlew.

The book is in two parts. The first part focuses on the brown hare and its habitat in the Derbyshire Dales. The second part looks at biodiversity and changing grassland management.

I have interviewed a number of farmers and landowners to gain an insight into the pressures they work under and the choices they have to make. Many farmers are involved in agri-environmental schemes that can help support wildlife. But it is clear that the fundamental changes in our countryside, brought about by intensive farming have been driven by governments acceding to pressure from agribusiness. We are all responsible for the pressures put on the land and its creatures by our demand for cheap food. Global forces as well as severe weather have put prices up but the true cost of our food can only be understood by seeing the bigger picture of land use both here in Britain and worldwide.

The current methods of loading both pasture and arable land with chemicals is unsustainable and destroying the natural fertility that this island was blessed with. The hare and the lapwing are telling us that by disappearing. Extinctions follow changing land use across the globe and the oil hungry business that farming has become adds to climate change that threatens us all.

People are out trying to count hares (not an easy task) but by the best estimates it seems that since the Biodiversity Action Plans were published in 1995, there are encouraging signs that the brown hare population has increased in some areas as a result of wildlife friendly farming practice. But the population has not yet doubled. While concern remains for this wonderful animal that is now extinct in certain areas of Britain, the hare has no legal protection and can be shot any day but Sunday and Christmas Day.

Christine Gregory
September 2010

In this International Year of Biodiversity, let us reflect on the root causes of biodiversity decline and take action to arrest it. Let us adjust policies and mindsets to reflect the true value of species and habitats. Let us recognize that biodiversity is life — our life. Let us act now to preserve it, before it is too late.

UN Secretary-General Ban Ki-moon's message
for the International Day for Biological Diversity on 22 May 2010

Part 1 The hare

The frisky one ...the slink-away ...the nibbler ...the fellow in the dew ...the friendless one ...the swift-as-the-wind ...the stalker ...the animal that no one dare name.

Just a few of the names used in a 13th century incantation, *The Names of the Hare*, delivered by hunters when going out to find this elusive animal.

No other creature in the British countryside has the iconic status of the hare. It has been associated with omens, madness, fertility, sanctity and witchcraft. It is the subject of myths, legends, poetry and art. You can see representations of hares in medieval churches, in stonework, windows and in tapestries. They appear in western art in religious works, hunting scenes or dead as motifs in still-life paintings. The hunted hare clearly had a value and meaning beyond its use as food or quarry and contemporary artists and sculptors still pursue the hare.

Hares appear in the earliest marks made by man on cave walls and they have remained culturally significant in many countries and societies right through until today. So what is it about the hare that has so fed the imagination of people across the world and over time?

The reality of the hare is, in many ways, as extraordinary as the myths that have built around it. Its athleticism is legendary. The brown hare can travel faster than a racehorse. It can jump high and wide. It is even a good swimmer. But, perhaps, its mythical status emanates from its strange and apparently contradictory behaviour.

The famously solitary hare will gather together in groups for purposes as yet unknown. They are highly-strung, timid creatures yet they seem to enjoy loud noise. They are said to enjoy thunderstorms and pet hares have been seen to drum on boxes for prolonged periods. For much of the time they are silent and yet will emit unearthly screams when in pain or distress. They race against cars and gather in large numbers on airfields and chase after jet aeroplanes on take off[1]. They will transform in a moment from being peaceful herbivores nibbling the grass to formidable figures standing high on two feet, boxing a would-be mate or rival.

Watching a hare going about its business, feeding on grasses and herbs, restlessly turning this way and that, apparently hesitant and indecisive, the label 'hare brained' is easy to understand. But when excited by fear or longing, its action is decisive and dynamic. As it flees or chases a mate or rival, then this most timid of creatures becomes a sinuous, bounding force of bone, muscle and sinew, defying logic, expectation and gravity.

What is a hare?

Hares are lagomorphs, a distinct group of animals which was only identified as such in 1912[2]. Apart from 30 little known species called pikas (a small hamster-like animal with rounded ears which lives in Asia and North America), all lagomorphs are either rabbits or hares. They are all herbivores and share similar digestive systems, ingesting their food twice over in order to extract greater nutritional value from it.

There are three species of hare in the British Isles – the blue or mountain hare (Lepus timidus), the Irish hare (Lepus timidus hibernicus) see Appendix 1, and the brown hare (Lepus europaeus). Two of these (the mountain hare and the more common brown hare) live in Derbyshire. This book is about the brown hare.

The mountain hare

The blue or mountain hare is an indigenous species that lives in upland areas, including the remote mountainsides and moors of the Highlands of Scotland and the Isle of Man. We are lucky to have here in Derbyshire the last population in the English mainland. Our local mountain hares live in the high moorland of the Dark Peak, where they were they were introduced by the Victorians to provide something in addition to grouse for the gentry to shoot.

Mountain hares are smaller than brown hares. They also have smaller ears. This reduces surface area and conserves heat.

In the summer, the mountain hare's pelage (coat) is a greyish brown which makes it easy to mistake for it for a rabbit at this time of year. In the winter, apart from the tips of its ears, it turns snow white or shades of brownish-grey to provide winter camouflage. But in winters with little snow, the mountain hare's striking white coat makes it extremely visible and thus vulnerable for part of the year. Unlike the brown hare, its tail is completely white all year round. Arctic and Greenland hares are considered the same species as the mountain hare.

These beautiful creatures are increasingly under threat. This is most likely the result of lost habitat and through over-grazing of heather moorland. However, they are also hunted, for sport and because they are host to a tick which carries a virus affecting commercial shooting of grouse.

The brown hare

The European brown hare is adapted to live in wide, open grassland or steppe country. After the ice age, grassy plains extended across Asia and Europe and the hare spread into these regions to become the dominant hare species throughout Europe and western Asia. The mountain hare had already settled into the arctic tundra left by the retreating glaciers while a land bridge connected Britain to the rest of Europe. But the brown hare was not present before sea levels separated the British Isles from mainland Europe.

It is thought that the brown hare arrived in Britain when it was introduced for religious purposes by the Celts[3]. It has been heavily exploited wherever it occurs, for sport and for its meat and pelt.

The brown hare is the largest of British hares and the fastest of all hares. It can reach speeds of up to 45 miles per hour. This is why it has been so valued as a game animal and persecuted down the ages through hunting on horseback and with hounds. It has also had its speed and wits tested against greyhounds, whippets and lurchers in the now illegal sport of hare coursing.

A hare once seen is hard to forget. At a distance racing across a field, a hare seems to be flowing over the ground in an element all its own, as if airborne. Its speed and effortless motion are unlike that of any other small animal and it can be mistaken for a bird in low, gliding flight.

The brown hare has a very distinctive appearance. It has a powerful rangy body with immensely long hind legs. Its face has strong features marked by contrasting lines of dark hair and patches of white hair. Its ears are longer than those of either the mountain hare or the rabbit.

An adult hare's face has a certain kind of solemn beauty. Its long, broad, almost Roman nose meets its entirely divided upper lip (hence the term 'hare-lip').

Its eyes are large and prominent and a striking amber colour. There is a curious coldness in a hare's stare despite the warmth of its golden iris.

The coat or 'pelage' is richly coloured with a range of hues from fawn and gold to a reddish brown. This redness is more apparent in winter when its shaggy outer hairs give it an almost leonine appearance. Individuals vary but all have white under parts and inner flanks. The chest has a particularly thick red 'mane', which withstands the opponent's claws in boxing matches.[4] The tail is white underneath with black hair on its top surface.

How to tell a rabbit from a hare

The Plantagenets first introduced the rabbit (Oryctolagus cuniculus) to Britain around 800 years ago. While hares have been here much longer, rabbits have proliferated in far greater numbers.

Hares do not 'breed like rabbits' or behave much like them either. There are some similarities and it is easy to confuse the two, but there are significant differences.

Hares are much bigger than rabbits weighing on average 5kg. The average weight of a full-grown rabbit is only 1.7kg.

Hares are between 54 and 60cm long. Buck rabbits are about 48cm.

While the hare is reddish brown, the rabbit is a dull greyish brown.

In winter the hare has a layer of coarse 'guard' hairs, the rabbit also has 'speckling' outer hairs but these are finer.

The hare's ears are spectacularly long. They are vividly marked at the back with white fur that contrasts with black tips.

The rabbit has a rounded face with dark eyes and it has short ears with no black tips.

The rabbit's tail is white all over and is a conspicuous bobbing white when it flees from danger, acting as a warning to other rabbits.

Two very different lives

Hares and rabbits live different lives, despite being closely related.

Rabbits are sociable creatures living in large colonies of family groups with linked underground burrows (warrens). Their young are born blind and naked, starting out their life in a burrow lined with fur pulled by the mother from her chest. The burrow provides a safe place for rearing young and it shelters the young rabbit from weather and predators.

This cosy start in life is in great contrast to the life of a hare, which is lived entirely out in the open from birth. A leveret is born fully furred, sighted and 'ready to go'. Its entire life is lived above ground.

Rabbits rarely move further than 150 metres from their home whereas hares range over quite large areas to search for food. How far they have to go depends on their particular habitat and territory. If suitable forage is hard to find, hares may travel as far as a kilometre to find what they need to eat[5].

The close social interaction and interdependence of rabbits led to the devastation in their numbers through the spread of the human-imported disease myxomatosis in the 1950s. This disease has had no impact on hare populations. The rabbit population has made a dramatic recovery and currently stands at around 40 million, roughly forty times the number of hares.

Rabbits are able to warn each other of danger and retreat to their burrows for safety. The hare relies entirely on its senses, camouflage and its immense speed to evade predators.

Where rabbits will scatter on retreat from danger, a hare will often sit tight and hunker down. When a hare does run for safety, it gradually accelerates from a loping gait to great leaping strides with its tail held low showing the black surface of the top side.

Life cycle of the hare

Hares have a long breeding season. Mating can begin as early as January and continue into autumn. The actual length of any one season depends largely on weather conditions. A mild winter will extend the breeding season and an unusually cold spring or early autumn will limit it. The weather is also critical to breeding success.

The gestation period of the hare is thought to be 41 – 42 days, but is hard to establish this precisely.

Does can have up to four litters in a year but three is more usual. Litters vary in size depending on the season, the weather, the age and condition of the doe, and of her food supply. There are usually one or two leverets in an early spring litter and three or four in litters born later in the summer. A warm spring will increase the size of litters. A warm summer will mean a higher number of pregnant does and, often, bigger litters.

At birth a leveret weighs on average 100 grams. By six months it will be fully grown, but a young hare will not usually breed in the year in which it was born. Once a litter is born, the buck plays no part in rearing or defending young.

The mortality rate of hares is high. Their life expectancy on farmland is, on average, only a year. Just half of the hares alive at the end of a summer will be alive the following spring and it seems to be the youngest that are the most vulnerable to the many hazards they face in the British countryside. Diseases of the hare, while important, are less significant to hare numbers than other factors (see Appendix 1).

Although most live only a short life, it has been known for hares to live for 12 years. However, this should be regarded as the maximum possible life expectancy. The maximum life span for most hares on British farmland is three to four years. But experience comes with age, and does are more successful and productive when they are older. As the majority of does fail to reach full maturity, the decline in hare numbers is easy to understand.

Predators

After man, the fox is the hare's principal predator. It mainly eats leverets, but when it can surprise one, it may take an adult hare. An uncontrolled population of foxes can cause devastation to a population of hares. Predation is more intense when there are low numbers of other small mammals. The only birds of prey capable of taking an adult hare are the golden eagle and goshawk.

Leverets are vulnerable to a range of predators including foxes, badgers, stoats, mink, owls and buzzards. The quality of cover such as hedgerows, crops and woodland is vital to the safety of both adults and leverets.

Badgers have become more common and may be significant predators of leverets. They are also known to eat the eggs and the young of ground-nesting birds, and to dig out young rabbits and other small mammals.

Population decline

At the start of the twenty first century the brown hare population in Britain was estimated to be around 750,000. Hare populations have been declining throughout Europe over the last 40 years. In Britain numbers had declined by about 75%.

It is currently thought that there has been a significant recovery in hare numbers in some areas. But it is unlikely that the UK Biodiversity Action Plan has achieved the target of doubling the spring population by the year 2010.

In 1880 the Ground Game Act was passed, which allowed tenants and landowners to kill hares throughout the year. At this point there were around four million brown hares in Britain. In 1996, just over a century later, the results were published of the first extensive national survey ever undertaken of the brown hare population (carried out by researchers at the University of Bristol for the Joint Nature Conservation Committee). It found that numbers had dropped by 80%[6]. After this numbers declined even further.

The distribution of Britain's remaining brown hares is uneven. Broadly speaking there is a west/east divide with greater densities of hares in the east.

By far the largest concentration of brown hares in Britain is in East Anglia, a predominantly crop growing area thought to have 20% of the British population, despite having only 5% of land area. In general, arable farmland has greater numbers of hares than pastureland. There are, however, some arable areas of Britain where there are no hares at all.

Live animal counts by researchers and various conservation bodies have only been undertaken over the past thirty years and counting hares is a complex business. One way of understanding the rate of decline in the population has been to measure the size of shooting bags. It seems that there were annual fluctuations in hare numbers before 1960 but after that there has been a more general and rapid decline[7]. There are several ways of accounting for this, but it is generally agreed that modern intensive farming methods are the most important cause.

In the Dales there is a significant population of brown hares. Derbyshire Wildlife Trust has collected data showing a wide distribution of hares across the county. While they are not numerous they appear to be holding their own, and even increasing in some areas.

Modern arable farming

Agricultural practice has altered dramatically over the last fifty years and this coincides with the decline of the brown hare throughout Europe and of the Irish hare.

This book focusses on hares that live in pastoral land and the particular difficulties they face in this landscape with the changing management of stock-grazed fields, silage production and the loss of wildflower meadows. It is also worth noting briefly, the impact of changes in arable farming methods as crop growing areas (especially East Anglia and lowland Scotland) have the densest population of hares in Britain. Changes in arable farming have had the most significant impact on overall hare numbers.

Intensive arable farming has meant hedges (valuable shelter for all wildlife) being grubbed out and the creation of vast open fields of single crops that can be farmed using large modern machinery. The size of the fields means that hares have to range further to find varied forage. Research has shown that hare numbers declined on farms where fields were enlarged – a practice adopted widely through the 1980s and 90s[8].

It is now common practice to sow cereals in the autumn instead of the spring, which means that crops ripen earlier and are too hard and woody for hares to eat. The practice of crop rotation has ceased in an era of chemical farming so that fields of cereal crops once harvested in August are left bare. This can lead to acute food shortages for hares into the autumn months.

To sustain monocultures, farmers have come to rely on herbicides, insecticides and fungicides sprayed from large booms across a broad area. Many of these chemicals are poisonous to wildlife, and hares sheltering in crops, particularly leverets, can receive several toxic doses. Hares lick these poisons and ingest them. The Hare Preservation trust has it on record that one farmer discovered thirty dead hares in his carrot field several hours after spraying.

The hare's habit of sitting tight when in danger can lead to death from chemical poisoning or destruction from the machinery itself. The now illegal practice of stubble burning also led to mortalities.

The European Union introduced payments to arable farmers in 1992 to 'set aside' land to address the problem of over production. This policy of taking fields out of use allowed wild plants to grow and was beneficial to hares and other wildlife. This policy ended in 2007. In the meantime numerous agro-environmental schemes have given grants to farmers to help them to improve wildlife habitats. See Part 2.

Courtship

The hare is a potent symbol of spring, the time of year when these normally elusive animals can be seen even in broad daylight, racing through fields, chasing each other or boxing. They can sometimes be seen in mysterious circles, which gives the appearance of ritualistic behaviour.

Courtship may start in January. It continues throughout the spring and summer months and continues on into the autumn.

Climate change may account for breeding this late in the year and there are welfare concerns over leverets born late in the season. They may become orphaned or suffer as the weather deteriorates. Most estates, farmers and those who shoot operate a voluntary 'close season' for hares from March until August (there is no legal 'open' and 'close season' as there is with other game creatures). This means that leverets or their mothers can be shot in the autumn and pregnant, or even lactating does (who may have litters very early), can be shot in February.

While mating antics continue through much of the summer, they become harder to observe. As the days lengthen, much of this activity is confined to early mornings and evenings. From mid April onwards, as the grass and crops grow, it is much harder to see hares.

Our image of the mad March hare owes as much to the visibility of hares at that time in the year as it does to seasonal changes in their behaviour.

Throughout the winter months hares need to conserve energy. Forage is scarce and survival depends on keeping energy output as low as possible. All year round, brown hares are mainly active at night while resting up in the daylight hours. As the days lengthen, their daytime activity increases and with warmer days and the start of new growth, they come into breeding condition.

The wild chases seen in spring are usually part of mating activity. Groups of hares begin to congregate in early spring – to mate, to feed on newly grown grass or crops and to integrate socially in ways which are not yet fully understood. As most does in a group come in to mating condition at around the same time, mating activity is more intense at this time.

Hares are polygamous and if a female is close to being ready to mate there may be several males following her. Females are only on heat for a few hours so males will compete with some fervour. They will attempt to mate with as many females as possible, often in rapid succession. There is no organised social ranking among loosely associated groups of hares, but it is thought that dominant males will have a greater chance of mating with more females.

Throughout the long breeding season hares can be seen in pairs. A doe is closely followed by a buck who will shadow her every move. This guarding behaviour can be sustained over days and lead to mating, flight by the doe, or boxing. The doe is very slightly larger than the buck and more than a match for him in a skirmish

Mating induces ovulation. A female may produce four or five eggs in response to mating, but further ovulation and mating can also happen during pregnancy. This results in hares having the remarkable capacity to carry potential litters of different ages at the same time. (Rabbits also continue to mate during pregnancy, but they cannot simultaneously carry pregnancies from more than one mating.)

This phenomenon is called superfoetation and it has been recorded in up to 13% of females in brown hare populations[9]. Historically, much has been made of this unusual reproductive capacity and it is one of many mysterious and magical properties attributed to the hare. It is one source of the symbolic association of the hare with fecundity and sexual potency.

Boxing

Boxing involves hares standing upright and actually punching at each other with their powerful front feet. They seem to be almost dancing as they constantly hop to maintain balance. These matches can involve competing males but are more often a female fighting off the unwanted attentions of a male. When several hares are gathered around, they can seem to be an audience for the fight, but usually the onlookers are other competing males waiting for an opportunity to mate.

Male and female hares are called respectively, does and bucks or jacks and jills. In the past, many people had strange ideas about the sex of hares, believing that all hares are female, that they change sex year by year or that the males could give birth. Up until recent times, many country people would refer to any hare as 'she'.[10]

Built for speed

The hare's anatomy and physiology are made for speed.

The hare's heart is six times larger in proportion to its body weight than that of a rabbit. It also has more blood than most animals.

Its lungs are large and it has wider nasal passages than a rabbit. This allows it to take in the good supply of oxygen needed to drive its powerful legs and muscular frame at great speed.

Its capacity to accelerate, to jump high and to change direction fast, are aided by the highly adapted muscles in its hind limbs.

Its furred front and back feet help it travel fast over a variety of terrain including wet grass, muddy ground and snow.

The hare moves at speed in a bounding action. The hind feet land ahead and either side of the fore feet, which touch the ground close together.

Senses

- The hare's senses are attuned to danger.

- The hare's eyes are high in its head and placed to the sides so that it has almost 360 degree vision. Its only blind spot is directly ahead of it.

- Hares are colour blind but able to see tonal variation and movement from almost any direction.

- The hare's huge ears can be moved separately to pick up sounds from different directions at once.

- The hare's sense of smell is highly developed and it is often the scent of the predator that first betrays it to the hare. On a windy day their problems in detecting scent can make them appear more restless and flighty.

The great escapist

The hare has been noted for its high intelligence as well as for its erratic behaviour. It is quite possible that the two are linked and that what appears to be strange behaviour is, in fact, a strategy to evade enemies. The hare has no refuge but its speed and wits. It has refined the art of escape.

Hares often escape by running uphill. They know that there is no predator that stands a chance of catching them.

In addition to their remarkable athleticism, they exploit their unique ability to change direction at high speed. Hares and leverets sometimes chase each other in tight circles or are seen running in a zig-zag pattern. While this is often part of courtship, it also gives the hare practice in getting away under the nose of a hound.

Hares are adept at laying false scent trails. They will double back or move away from the trail at right angles only to return. They also make wide sideways jumps so that a scent trail will seem to end. They do this when returning to their form, or when going to feed leverets, so that a predator will have a harder time tracing their exact location. This strategy will buy the hare time as the predator approaches.

In the Derbyshire Dales, hares make extensive use of walls both for shelter and escape routes. Often their paths can be seen running adjacent to walls or diagonally across fields to gateways. They make use of escape holes and are adept at climbing over walls or perching on top of them to look out for danger.

Hares know their territory very well and follow familiar routes, sometimes along paths that have been worn down by generations of hares.

This hare sits in a path through a meadow.

Where hares live

As Neolithic man cleared the primeval forests, the new areas of open land were exploited by the brown hare, and it spread westwards from Asia into Europe. The hare's association with farmland and to man's activities goes back to the earliest cultivation of crops and domestication of stock.

When the brown hare first came to Britain around 2000 years ago, much of lowland Britain was being farmed. Since that time, the hare's natural habitat has remained farmland and open pasture.

Hares make use of different habitat features. What suits them ideally is a mixed and diverse landscape that includes pasture, a range of crops, woodland, hedgerows and hay meadows. The mixed farms of the Victorian era, with a patchwork of small fields with hedgerows and crops grown in rotation, was the ideal landscape for hares, providing year-round forage and shelter.

In the Joint Nature Conservation Committee survey of the brown hare population in 1996, arable areas were assessed as having nearly three times the number of hares as pastureland.

In the Derbyshire Dales hares are under some pressure as a lot of the land is quite intensively managed. Hares are attracted to what remains of the unimproved wildflower meadows, or other uncultivated areas such as farm tracks, field margins, banks and dale sides. However, while these areas are clearly important to hares, they are not extensive enough to support high numbers. It seems that they will live in or near unimproved pasture, but they are most often seen in the far more widespread areas of semi-improved pasture or in the great expanses of ryegrass that now dominate much of this landscape.

Individuals sometimes form loose associations with other hares.
Groups can be seen in the daytime in spring and summer, resting,
feeding and grooming in the same field.

Quite often hares sit just below the brow of a hill or on the margins of fields that border on the dales.

The terrain of the Derbyshire Dales is ideal for hares, as the hillsides and wide open spaces allow them to see any predator approaching.

In the daytime hares are mainly at rest, very often in the shallow scrape known as a form. This depression in the earth is dug so that most of the hare's body is hidden from view.

Home ranges

Hares rest up in areas that are a kind of base within what is called their 'home range'. But these areas will change according to season and weather.

In winter, in bad weather or on hot sunny days, woodland is used for daytime shelter. The high limestone plateau of the Derbyshire Dales has few trees. However, there are shelter belts and other small wooded areas that provide important shelter and cover.

The dales themselves are an important landscape feature for hares and for other wildlife as the steep sides are undisturbed by people and provide tree and shrub cover. They are almost entirely unimproved and species-rich and so full of nutritious forage.

The extent of individual hares' home ranges varies considerably. In intensively farmed arable areas hares are often forced to travel further to find food if large fields are left bare or there are unsuitable crops. In a study by the Game Conservancy Council on a mixed arable and livestock farm in Hampshire, hares were radio tracked up to a period of seven months. Individual animals showed wide variations in their home ranges of between 17 and 72 hectares, but around 40 hectares was the average[11].

In pasture areas, hares often have large home ranges in order to get nutritious forage. How far they travel varies with the season. Hares range over larger areas in winter and spring than they do in summer and autumn.

Hares mainly feed at night on whatever is available in season. If the forage is near to their resting place they may have no need to travel far, but sometimes they have to go a long way to feed.

In the few places that cereal crops are grown in the Derbyshire Dales, they act as a magnet to hares.

In summer tall, dense crops shelter adults and leverets. In the winter, ploughed furrows provide good places for hares to settle in a form and they become almost invisible against the earth.

Pastureland that is not grazed in the summer is mainly grown for silage, which is cut up to three times in the growing season, causing both disturbance and damage to adult hares and leverets.

Hares that live in pastureland tend to be smaller and in poorer condition than those in arable areas[12]. This means in turn, that they are less successful in reproducing.

In most areas of Britain, refuge and shelter provided by hedgerows has been severely reduced. It is thought that hedgerows provide a corridor along which hares and other mammals can move between territories. Across Britain, it has been suggested that 150,000 miles of hedgerow have been lost since the war.

Rest areas are extremely important to hares as they need to find places that are reasonably secure from predators with an open view, some cover and protection from prevailing winds. It is even more vital that they have safe areas in which to leave their young.

What hares eat

Hares are entirely vegetarian and they thrive on a varied diet. Biodiversity in plant life is important to them. They are particular about what they eat, preferring new, tender growth in grasses, herbs and crops. They will also eat fruits, flower buds and seeds, which are particularly nutritious as they contain protein and fats.

In the Derbyshire Dales and other pasturelands hares do best where there are pockets of unimproved wildflower meadow. This species-rich and diverse habitat supports them both because of the nutritional value of the forage and the varied cover it provides.

They will eat all grasses, including the modern varieties of ryegrass grown for silage, though they are known to prefer the older types of wild grasses. The widespread application of herbicides and nitrogen fertilisers to improve grassland, both coarsens growth and eliminates variety and nutritional value.

In winter hares have to live mainly on wild grass, though they eat winter wheat and root vegetables if they are available. They will also eat tree bark, buds and shoots, which can be very destructive in woodland.

Hares have a high metabolic rate and they carry little in the way of body fat. To remain healthy they need a good supply of food all year round.

In the daytime, hares digest the forage from the night before and excrete soft faeces, which are immediately eaten in order to extract greater nutrition. Once they have extracted all the nutrients from their twice-digested food, they excrete hard pellets at night that are then discarded.

How and where to see hares

The Derbyshire Dales, in particular the limestone plateau, is hare country. The extensive open grasslands, the wide vistas and the remote hilltops provide hares with the space and open views that they need to see and to escape from predators.

Seeing a hare silhouetted against the skyline, wandering along a farm track or racing across a field somehow completes the view and takes us deeper into the experience of being in this landscape.

The elusiveness of the hare means that for many people a fleeting glimpse of one is an intensely memorable experience, providing a momentary link to a world that we feel in danger of losing. The hare has become iconic in our culture and that of many other societies. Its purity of form, speed, unique appearance and strange behaviour combine to give it almost mystical properties in our collective imagination.

The hare is an animal of extremes. It endures rain, wind, snow and frost and exists in a way that suggests a pure connection to the landscape. It is a living, moving part of the open grasslands on which it depends and seeing a hare confirms our sense that wildness endures in the midst of a landscape shaped by people.

It is possible to see a hare at any time of day throughout the year, but it is also possible to walk in hare country and never see one at all. The hare scene after dark is very different from during the daytime and farmers going to check over their stock at night report seeing large numbers of hares congregating to feed where in daylight there are none. Sadly, poachers and illegal hare coursers know where and how to find hares at night by using strong lamps to temporarily blind them and then shoot, catch or course them.

Hares are very shy animals, and are easily disturbed. They are extremely wary of their main predator – man, and they will not tolerate much disturbance, so you are unlikely to encounter hares close to public footpaths in broad daylight.

It can be harder to see them as the grass and crops grow. Cattle are turned out in May and hares retreat away from heavily grazed pasture to more remote areas or to field margins.

Hares rest in a position from which they can see any potential threat. Their profile in the form makes it very hard to see them and their long low-lying shape can easily be mistaken for a molehill, a clod of earth or a piece of dung. The hare's camouflage is very effective and you will need binoculars to scan a field for a brown shape that may miraculously burst into life.

Once silage or hay is cut, hares are visible once more, foraging in the grass leys for fresh growth. They seem to be drawn to open country that gives them a chance to exercise their immense speed, untrammelled by the denser growth of summer.

The nocturnal habits of hares mean that dawn and dusk remain the best times to see them as they move to or from their daytime rest areas.

A hare will remain hunkered down hoping not to be seen until the very last moment when, feeling threatened, it will spring up and move off at speed or retire to a safe distance to assess the danger and best escape routes.

It is this moment of assessment, which signals to a predator that the hare has seen it. It is also the moment that provides the photographer or the hunter with an opportunity for a shot.

It is easier to watch young hares than adults as they have not fully developed the vigilant senses that they will need to survive.

A guide to watching hares

If you know where there are hares or you've spotted them in the past you will want to give yourself the best chance of seeing them again. Before you set out you will need to be aware of how the hare employs all of its senses to protect it.

- There is no substitute for being up early or out late.

- Do not stray onto private land. You can see hares in open country, even near to popular footpaths, once all the visitors have gone home.

- Be quiet and keep dogs under control

- Wear clothing that is tonally 'quiet' and that doesn't provide a strong contrast with the landscape.

- Take binoculars and scan the area around you very carefully.

- Move slowly and avoid sudden movement or large gestures.

- Move while the hare is eating or going away from you as its view of you is obstructed.

- If you remain absolutely still on seeing a hare it is possible that it will come very close to you.

- Notice the wind direction and position yourself so that your scent is not blowing towards the hare.

- If you are upwind of the hare you can use walls as a barrier to your scent in order to gain a closer view.

- Always move towards hares against the prevailing wind. Wind can help you as this disguises sound.

- Scent will betray your presence. If the ground is wet from rain or dew, scent carries more, whereas dry conditions make hare spotting easier.

- As with most wildlife watching, patience is the key. Sitting quietly in the vicinity of hares is more likely to provide memorable viewing than moving about looking for them.

A hare may seem oblivious to your presence, which has led some observers to think that their sight is poor. The position of its prominent eyes gives it a wide-angle view on either side and (almost) literally eyes in the back of its head.

Its view head-on is limited. If a hare is moving towards you, if you are down wind of it and your silhouette is not against the skyline, it may just keep coming.

Hares and grazing stock

Hares that live in the pastures of the Derbyshire Dales share their domain with sheep and cattle. When the grass grows lush in May, cattle are turned out to graze. Quiet fields that had been occupied almost exclusively by hares from October onwards are transformed by roaming cattle.

Hares do not like to be in close proximity to cattle for a variety of reasons and research has shown that they move out of grazed areas. When cattle move in, hares move on.

It is harder for hares to settle and rest in the presence of cattle. A research study in the early 1980s conducted by scientists from the Game Conservancy Council and Southampton University Biology Department analysed the behaviour of hares in relation to cattle. They looked at the density of hares in stocked and unstocked fields through the year in the hours after dawn and dusk and at night. They found that hare densities were much higher in unstocked fields than stocked and that hare numbers would drop when stock was moved in. When stock was removed, hares would return. Their numbers built over several days reaching a peak after nine days.

The researchers also looked at hare behaviour when cattle were present and noted that they 'spent less time feeding, more time crouched down, and were more likely to flee'.

Researchers Barnes, Tapper and Williams concluded: 'The effect of livestock on hares' behaviour shows that it is the disturbance caused by stock to the hares' normal activities that causes them to avoid these fields (and)...effectively reduces the area of grass that is available to hares.' They further surmised that hares would be forced into sharing limited space elsewhere and that the high density that results 'may raise the rate of disease transmission between individuals'[13].

Hares appear to be more relaxed in the presence of sheep as they pose far less of a threat and hares are accustomed to their presence all year round. It is common to see hares moving around sheep in the pastures of the Derbyshire Dales. On the other hand, sheep graze more efficiently than cattle, biting very close to the ground, leaving no forage for hares.

In the summer evenings hares can often be seen in newly mown fields.

Mating activity continues throughout the summer.

Leverets

A doe will give birth in a sheltered area, avoiding woodland or hedgerows that are the haunt of predators such as foxes, stoats and owls. Long grass, cereal crops and, especially, traditional hay meadows provide good cover for leverets.

When the litter is born, the tiny furred and sighted leverets are left in some cover for their mother to visit at dusk. A few days after birth, she disperses the litter to evade predators. It is thought that the doe calls her young together for their nightly feed as several leverets have been seen to suckle at the same time, having moved together from their separate hiding places. This feed of protein-rich milk takes place just once every 24 hours, at dusk.

Does try to protect the leverets' whereabouts from predators by creating baffling routes that involve back tracking and jumping to confuse the scent trail. Apart from these nightly visits, the leveret just sits tight, alone in its form with only cover, camouflage and stillness to protect it. However, there are many accounts of the doe, called by the screams of her young, attempting to defend leverets against attack from predators[14].

A doe will nurse her leverets for between 20 and 30 days, usually stopping when another litter comes along. Once a leveret has been weaned, it is left to fend for itself. They are extremely vulnerable in these early weeks and the mortality rate is high. The hare's habit of sitting tight and hunkering down to avoid being seen, instilled from birth, has not served it well with mowing machines and combine harvesters. When silage, hay or cereal crops are cut, there can be a heavy toll of leverets.

The only thing about intensive farming that I think would effect hares is the difference between silaging and haymaking. Silaging starts in mid May, whereas hay is cut at the earliest in mid June. It gives the little ones a chance to get going a bit better. And tackle's bigger. Obviously mowers are bigger. Our mower is twelve feet and you go that much faster, it whizzes that much ground up in one go. And do they get a chance to get out of the way? We used to hay make with a four foot mower. A hare can hear the tractor long before the mower gets there. We stop if we see a hare. But we don't necessarily see a leveret that's hiding in the grass. Keith Harrop – farmer

While being nursed, leverets have only cover and camouflage to protect them. Later they have to learn to rely on their senses and speed to escape from danger.

A young hare pays close attention to the condition of its feet by spreading its long toes wide apart.

Hares are fastidious in their grooming and can sometimes be seen washing themselves much as a cat does.

In the summer, the young hare has to feed on the plentiful and varied forage of the season in order to survive the lean autumn and winter months.

Vehicles on country roads kill large numbers of hares and leverets. Hares are especially vulnerable when crossing roads to reach different feeding areas at night. It is remarkable that a young animal with so little exposure to its parent can learn all the survival skills it will need through its short life. It is easy to see why so few survive into adulthood.

In autumn hares grow their thick pelage ready for a winter lived outside. As temperatures drop they will make the most of any sunshine and rest up in day time to conserve energy.

Before winter crops begin to grow, grasses growing through the stubble provide nutritious forage.

Hares and field sports

Hares have been exploited for their speed, grace and intelligence for over three thousand years. They have been prized in particular for their value as quarry for hunting by hounds, for coursing and for shooting. They were pitted against dogs bred especially to compete with them by Chinese emperors and the ancient Egyptians. 'Sight hounds', familiar from mediaeval art and looking very like the modern greyhound, were most likely introduced to Britain from Celtic mainland Europe in the fifth or sixth century. These dogs were valued for their acute eyesight in open country and for speed that could compete with that of the hare.

Hares and the law

Today hares have only limited protection under British law. There is no close season for the hare, which can be shot at any time apart from Sundays or on Christmas Day. Other restrictions apply regarding the killing of hares on moorland and unenclosed land.

In some contexts, hare are regarded as game, in others as an agricultural pest. Highly prized as game for hunting from mediaeval times, the hare was protected so that only elites such as royalty, landed gentry and senior church figures were allowed to hunt for it. A succession of monarchs imposed laws to protect hares from poachers and illegal hare coursers, but this was to do with conserving a plentiful supply for their own enjoyment of hunting or coursing. See Appendix 3.

The Hunting Act of 2004 made it illegal to hunt wild animals with dogs and outlawed hare coursing in Great Britain. While hunting and coursing are now illegal in England, Scotland and Wales, they continue in the Republic of Ireland. Since 2002 hares have been protected from coursing and hunting in Northern Ireland under a special protection order. This is currently under review.

Shooting hares remains legal throughout Britain and Ireland.

Hunting with dogs

Packs of dogs have long been used to hunt for hares. Beagle packs and basset hounds were followed on foot while harriers were used while hunting hares on horseback. Before the ban made hunting illegal there were around 100 packs of hounds dedicated to hunting hares in Britain.

The High Peak Harriers were a hunting pack dedicated to hunting the hare in the Derbyshire Dales. The pack of harriers, which was established in 1848 is still based in Bakewell. Since the hunting ban, the hunt still meets to go drag hunting.

Hare coursing

Coursing is an ancient sport involving greyhounds but also borzois, salukis, whippets, deerhounds or lurchers competing to reach or turn a hare. This was an immensely popular sport commanding huge crowds and attracting big prizes. The biggest event in England was the Waterloo Cup, which attracted a crowd of 10,000 in its last year before coursing was made illegal by the 2004 Act.

The rules of coursing varied according to the different ways it was undertaken. The two main types of coursing were open coursing, which took place in an open field, and closed or park coursing, which still takes place in the Republic of Ireland (see Appendix 3).

In open coursing, a person called a 'slipper' released two greyhounds once a hare was driven past. The hare was given a 100 yard head start before the dogs were released, as the dogs are able to run at 55mph over a short distance compared with the hare's 45 mph maximum speed.

The hare's ability to turn fast and switch direction tested the speed and skills of each dog. Points were awarded and the dog that gained the most would then go on to compete with other dogs in a knock-out competition.

Supporters of hare coursing are eager to point out that hares often got away. However, many were killed, either torn apart by dogs or badly injured. It has been argued that the traumatic ordeal of being subjected to a race for its life against large dogs amid loud crowds of shouting people led to the death of many hares from shock after the event.

Since hare coursing was made illegal in mainland Britain, the sport has persisted illegally and this has led to organised gangs catching hares for coursing, often by 'lamping' at night. Illegal coursing events using either greyhounds or lurchers have continued to attract large and often belligerent crowds. The activity attracts money and is a highly organised crime, which does considerable harm to farmland as well as to hares. Farmers have come under threat from poachers and coursers and this has had the unfortunate effect of some farmers attempting to destroy the population of hares on their land in order to deter the menace of those intent on this criminal activity. This has had in turn, a severely detrimental effect on hare numbers in some parts of the country[15].

Each outcry of the hunted hare
A fibre from the brain does tear[16]

William Blake

If you shoot a hare and don't kill it, the noise is
horrendous. It's just like a baby squealing.
I don't shoot them now because they got scarce.

Keith Harrop – farmer

Shooting

Despite their rate of decline, both the mountain hare and the brown hare do not have protected status and they can still be shot for sport and/or as a pest.

The hare is seen as game in some parts of the country and as an agricultural pest in others. It is highly prized on many estates as quarry on organised shoots, which make a significant contribution to estate income.

Shooting estates are managed in such a way that game birds and hares can find shelter in the form of cover, maintained hedgerows, and woodland. These are places designed to attract and maintain game. Importantly, gamekeepers are employed to protect game creatures from predators..

The time for hare 'culls' or big estate shoots is February, just after pheasant shooting has finished. This is especially significant in East Anglia where large and highly organised shoots on farms or estates are commonplace. The February shoots in this region alone can significantly reduce the population of brown hares in England.

Driven hare shoots involve lines of beaters with guns spread around a large area of land moving in towards a line of standing guns, thus encircling all of the hares. Hares that attempt to run back, are shot by beaters. 'Up to 69% of the [local brown] hare population is killed in one shoot'[17].

The Victorians prided themselves on bags of well over a thousand a day of both brown hare in lowland areas and mountain hare in the Highlands.

The commercial value of hares in the fur trade was considerable. The Dumfries Fur Market was a major centre for the trade in Britain and the number of brown hare skins on sale there peaked at 70,000 in 1860[18].

The scale of senseless destruction during the Victorian and Edwardian period is now blamed for the decimation of many of our most cherished species of birds as well as animals. These days many estates claim that their management is aimed at conservation, but recently extravagant bags of many hundreds of hares have been recorded in the shooting estates of East Anglia. The recovery in hare numbers in these densely populated areas has been used to justify these killing sprees. But the reasons for the recovery are not straightforward.

When many hares are shot, a large percentage of the resident population is eliminated, but large numbers will then move in from elsewhere to make use of the increased forage and ideal conditions available after the shoot. Apparently stable populations in some areas therefore come at a cost to other areas which sustain losses. This pattern increases the distorted cluster effect of current population distribution. Some estates have had to limit or postpone their shoots owing to the growing overall scarcity of hares.

While the commercial value of hare meat is no longer much of a consideration, approximately 137,000 dead hares were exported per year during the late 1980s[19].

The 'mixed bag' shoot is more of a feature in areas where the hare is not so plentiful. Here hares are often part of the hunting bag along with other species which few people are ever privileged to see, such as woodcock, snipe and grey partridge.

While hares are not favoured by everyone who shoots, foreign visitors are enthusiastic about shooting them and will pay a high price for the privilege. Some Scottish estates let shoots to overseas visitors to bag mountain hares in the Highlands.

In the 1930s there were absolutely hundreds of hares about. My grandfather would tell you how they used to herd them into about a 40 acre field; 150 or 200 at a time, surround them and then unfortunately slaughter them. It was how they used to cull them. They spent all day herding them into one area and then had a shoot. That was part of the way of life, but that's in years gone by

Mark Swindell – farmer

Owing to the relatively low density and fragility and of the hare population in the Derbyshire Dales, the kind of shoots that are still common in East Anglia and that Mark Swindell describes no longer occur in this area.

Does sport help to preserve hares?

There is considerable discussion about the connections between hare population density and sporting activity. Many landowners and hunting and shooting enthusiasts argue that culls maintain healthy populations of hares (despite the indiscriminate nature of the shoot) and that hunting and, previously, coursing ensured a good level of care for the hares that provide the sport. One of the key arguments is that predator control by gamekeepers helps to maintain hare populations. There are now only a tenth of the gamekeepers operating in Britain compared with the number before the First World War. This has led to a rise in fox numbers and claims by some that hares can only flourish where gamekeepers are employed to protect game birds and hares from predation.

There is certainly a correlation between high densities of hares and areas with gamekeepers, but the reasons for this are complex. Research by a team from Bristol University in 1996 showed that there was 'no clear effect of changing fox populations either locally or nationally on brown hare numbers, and the benefits of a gamekeeper in terms of increased hare numbers appears to be due, at least in part, to the preservation of hare populations and the protection they receive from poachers. The Bristol team concluded that farmers who benefit from the vigilance of gamekeepers are more relaxed about the presence of hares and do not resort to culling them[20].

However three research studies in different locations over a period of years showed that control of common predators resulted in an increase in hare population density and allowed for long-term population growth. When predator control ceased there was a rapid decline in hare numbers[21]. These studies clearly demonstrated the benefits to both hare and partridge populations of the activities of a gamekeeper.

Another factor that accounts for high hare numbers is the richness of habitat associated with managed estate lands. However strong the connection is between sporting interests and conservation, the activity could be seen as self-limiting. More hares are protected so that more can be shot. The fact that the brown hare has been designated by the UK Biodiversity Action Plan a 'priority species of conservation concern' is hard to reconcile with the estimated 200,000 – 300,000 that are currently shot each year according to National Game Bag Census Data.

Winter survival

The survival of hares in winter depends on their ability to adapt to the harshest of conditions and to avoid the attentions of hungry predators. Their winter pelage is different from the summer as they develop long, coarse guard hares that provide extra protection against cold together with a dense soft undercoat. This gives them quite a shaggy appearance and the illusion of a more chunky build. Hares' feet are densely covered in fur that provides insulation against the cold and makes moving across snow easier. In the harshest of winters the hare will sit tight as the snow falls around it to create a kind of igloo for shelter.

When resting up in daytime, a brown hare in its form is easy to spot in shallow snow, having lost its effective camouflage. Of course, the mountain hare has this problem in reverse. Its perfect camouflage in snow is lost when the snow melts. Its white winter pelage then makes it highly visible.

It is easy to follow a hare's fresh tracks in the snow (see opposite) and this is why Henry VIII, who admired the hare as quarry, introduced a law forbidding the tracking and killing of hares in snow. He wanted to give them a sporting chance.

In arable areas, winter wheat and root vegetable crops provide valuable forage, but for hares in pastural land, grass is the main food in winter. It is hard for us to imagine how a hare can feed on frozen grass in the bitter temperatures of a winter's night.

In snow-covered fields you can sometimes see patches that hares have scratched in the ground to get at the meagre grass beneath. They also eat buds and bark and foresters sometimes regard them as a nuisance as they can ring bark young trees and kill them.

Access to woodland for food, shelter and escape from people is important to hares all year round but especially so in winter. They will take their chances with the predators that share the woods to get away from the worst of the winds, rain and snow.

Many hares in the Derbyshire Dales live high on the limestone plateau at around 1000 feet. Winter temperatures at these levels can remain below freezing all day, with wind chill lowering the temperature still further. Persistently harsh conditions such as those in 2009/10 take their toll on hare numbers. The youngest and lightest are the most vulnerable. Having survived this, in many parts of the country they then face the guns in February.

Creature of myth and magic

The hare has symbolised many things to many different peoples across the globe. Some of the northern European legends, fables and myths about hares are echoed in Africa, Japan, China, India, Mexico and North America.

The hare and the moon

The association between the hare and the moon is universal. The ancient Egyptian moon god Un-Nefer had the head of a hare, and the 'Great Hare' was worshipped by the Algonquin people, who believed the hare deity created the sun, moon and the earth. A Buddhist myth has the hare jumping into fire as a sacrifice to feed a starving visitor (who is a god in disguise). The hare is rewarded for this selflessness by being rescued and put on the moon. The immortal moon hare is celebrated in China and appears as an icon in both Hindu and Buddhist faiths.

A possible explanation for the link between the hare and the moon is that hares are most often seen on moonlit nights.

People who regarded the natural and spiritual world as one would naturally connect the two. Like the moon, the hare came to represent birth, growth, death and renewal.

The moon is inconsistent, appearing at a different place in the sky at different times each night. The hare also appears unexpectedly, behaves erratically and seems to disappear from the countryside for sustained periods.

The word lunacy comes from 'lunar'. The connections between the moon and madness and between the hare and madness are well established.

The hare in religion

The hare was a sacred animal to the Ancient Britons, who would not hunt or kill it. The Celts, who are thought to have first brought the brown hare to Britain, worshipped the hare and it played an important part in the springtime festival of Beltane, the only time at which the hare could be killed and eaten.

The Anglo-Saxon goddess Eostre is linked to Easter with the hare as the attendant spirit of the goddess. The appearance of lapwing's eggs and of leverets in the grasslands in springtime may have led to a belief that hares laid eggs. April was called Eostur-monath, or Dawn Month, completing a symbolic chain of association between the spring, renewal of life and the hare's unusual fertility, high level of activity and visibility at this time.

The hare's connection to Easter may have started in pre-Christian religions and the hunted hare became a Christian icon linked to the Crucifixion and Resurrection as a symbol of suffering, sacrifice and renewal.

There are several references to the hare in the Bible and different saints were said to have saved hares from the hunt. Hares are also evident in various symbolic representations in churches – hunted by dogs, feeding on grapes, in the clutches of an eagle or in a motif of three hares running in a ring with three ears linked at the centre. This motif, once thought to represent the holy trinity, is an ancient archetype found in medieval churches in England and Germany, in synagogues throughout Europe and in Buddhist and Islamic places of worship in the Middle and Far East.

The hare as witch

The hare is associated with many myths and superstitions. Some of them derive from a belief that witches could turn themselves into hares. There is evidence of this belief in the early Middle Ages and there are accounts recorded by Evans and Thomson in the 1970s.

The persecution of witches in the sixteenth and seventeenth centuries was aimed at stamping out the old religions and demonising any behaviour of women that was seen to be strange. This might be the power to heal with knowledge of herbs, a solitary way of life, unconventional behaviour or simply being old.

Hares had already been connected to lustfulness and sin as well as to innocence and purity in the Christian Church. Suddenly, with the anti-witch crazes, the hare's strange and apparently ritualistic behaviour fuelled superstition. It is easy to see how a creature that joins with others in congregations, that stands like a person, fights with its 'fists' and can cry like a child could be seen as a person disguised in animal form. One account of finding a witch-hare involves a young woman emerging from a hole in a hedge where a hare had disappeared while being hunted. The woman was out of breath and this 'proved' that she was a witch-hare.

There are innumerable stories of enchanted hares, magical hares and hares that are ill omens.

Part 2 Biodiversity

Wild flower meadows

Grasslands that have not been ploughed, reseeded or treated in any way over a period of decades can be classified as unimproved meadow. Such meadows were traditionally used for the production of hay. They contain a wide diversity of plant species and were once an integral part of the British countryside. They sustained a complete ecosystem.

Such meadows were hundreds of years in the making, supporting as many as 50 plant species in just one square metre and many more in total. A rich variety of insects, birds and animals not only relied on the meadow plants as a food source but also depended on the cover afforded by them to raise their young.

It is hard to comprehend the extent of the loss of wildflower meadows across the country. Natural England has estimated that we had lost 97% of species-rich meadow by 1996. The greatest period of loss was from the mid 80s to the mid 90s.

The web of life sustained in such areas provided a delicate balance of interdependent species. In agricultural terms, the hay provided winter fodder for sheep, cattle and horses and was valued as essential to the seasonal needs of sustainable farming. However, pressure to mechanise and intensify land use has meant the wide-spread practice of switching from hay and beet as winter fodder to using silage.

The grass developed for this purpose is a fast growing species of rye grass. Silage was once stored in high towers (silos), now it is wrapped and stored in large plastic-covered bundles which are a far cry from the haystacks of old. When hay was cut only in the summer months, the long grass provided refuge for small animals and birds for much of the breeding season. Now the frequent cutting of silage from May onwards can be damaging to ground-nesting birds and to leverets, despite farmers' best attempts at avoiding them.

There are other problems with rye grass. It is a monoculture that dominates and eliminates other species. Fields where it grows are treated with nitrogen-rich fertiliser, which alters for decades the structure of the soil and the possibilities of what can grow there.

In some areas, hedges have been grubbed out and stone walls removed to accommodate vast mowing machines. The resulting green deserts of ryegrass that are now a feature of sheep and cattle country mirror the prairie-like fields of arable areas.

In the Peak District National Park active conservation measures have preserved the ancient field patterns, preventing silage growing and cutting from entirely taking over the appearance of the landscape. But what can appear to be meadows rich with wildflowers are semi-improved pasture which are impoverished by successive application of fertiliser or muck spreading, which increases nitrogen levels in the soil and the dominance of certain weedy plants like dandelion, creeping buttercup and sorrel. Just one application of nitrogen fertiliser can destroy a wildflower meadow for decades to come. In the Derbyshire Dales there are subtle gradations of improvement and very different levels of biodiversity from field to field.

Modern types of rye grass are used because they grow fast and vigorously. Their yield is so high that they can be cut as many as three times in the growing season. They are not vulnerable to summer downpours in the way that hay was and neither is the cutting too dependent on good weather.

Once rye grass has been sown, if left alone unfertilised or altered in any way, it would take 50 years for a species-rich wildflower meadow to re-establish itself naturally with the help of only birds and the wind[22].

Why wildflower meadows matter

When you stray into a wildflower meadow, or explore a bank or daleside of unimproved pasture, you can sense a kind of magic. Grasses grow at different levels, each with a distinct layer of shifting airy density. Through the grasses shine the colours of a profusion of flowers. As the year progresses, a rich sequence of changes takes place as ranges of flowers succeed each other.

Every area in Britain once had its own unique selections of wildflowers depending on the soil type, geology and altitude.

The Derbyshire Dales have an especially rich selection of plant species associated with the limestone bedrock.

While the grass is low in early spring, bright early purple orchids are seen in the limestone grasslands along with meadow saxifrage, cuckoo flower, and cowslips.

Through May, buttercups, ox-eye daisies, vetches, hay rattle, sorrel and, in damp areas, ragged robin warm the colours of grassland. Close to the ground, on dalesides and banks grazed by sheep, flowers such as lady's mantle, eye bright, salad burnet, wild thyme and rock roses grow.

In later summer, loftier plants such as harebells, lady's bedstraw, field scabious, meadow cranesbill and knapweed are succeeded by betony, centaury and thistles which mingle with the tall grasses of the meadows.

The delicacy and richness of this abundance of wild growth is hard to exaggerate. It is the sound, as well as the sight and smell of wildflower meadows, that can be overwhelming.

Heavy bumblebees clamber into delicate harebells; flowers and grasses flicker with myriad butterflies, moths, and the occasional damselfly. Later in the summer, the larger, more majestic butterflies, the peacock, red admiral, comma and tortoiseshell mingle with the smaller butterflies and day flying moths. Through and around all this is the continuous murmur and hum of innumerable hoverflies grasshoppers, flies and bees.

The wildflower meadows were a seething mass of life that was once our quintessential countryside. Finding such a place now in the Derbyshire Dales – a bank too steep to mow or fertilise, the unworkably steep dale sides and the few conserved, unimproved wild flower meadows – is like discovering an oasis.

All wildlife thrives in wildflower meadows, including those summer
visitors that rely on insects to feed their young such as swallow,
swift, blackcap, flycatchers, whitethroat and redstart.

Farmland birds of the Dales

Farmland birds and hares have, historically, shared the same territory. Many of the landscape features that are conducive to the maintenance of vigorous hare numbers also support ground-nesting birds.

In March, curlew, lapwing and skylark nest then raise their young in the pastures, marshy areas or the moors of the Peak District. The hare's habitat of open grassland on the limestone plateau is also the habitat of these ground-nesting birds. Like the hare, the birds favour species-rich pasture that has a range of cover where they can feed on insects and invertebrates that thrive there.

The wild, tumbling call of the curlew and the distinctive cry of the peewit (the sound that furnished the name) were sounds of the returning spring not just on the high moors but on the pastures of the White Peak as well.

Larks are on the wing from February until July, the 'blithe spirits' whose song is the defining sound of open country. These birds, together with the resident grey (or English) partridge are natural companions to the hare; the sight and sound of them have been linked for centuries.

The main periods of decline in both farmland birds and hares coincide with greatest periods of agricultural change (see Appendix 4). In the Peak District this includes drainage of wet pasture on moorland fringes, but most widespread and particular to the Derbyshire Dales is the ploughing up of much of the remaining unimproved pasture and the destruction of the flower-rich hay meadows.

In the Peak District National Park 50% of the hay meadows were lost between 1985 and 1996, and a further 25% were lost or went into decline between 1995 and 1998.

The rye grass monoculture does not support the level of insect life that waders, skylarks and partridge need to rear their young successfully. As the ground loses its fertility, the beetles, larvae and invertebrates needed to feed nestlings become scarcer.

In addition there is now almost routine use of antibiotics in cattle that are prone to infection in intensive farming systems. The dung from treated cattle is sterile thereby reducing the presence of the beetles, bugs, worms and grubs that are a food source to birds of the meadows. It also fails to break down organically and nourish the soil.

What's good for hares is good for us

Species-rich grasslands were once enmeshed in British farming culture. They were part of a sustainable system for producing food and managing the land   Graham Harvey, The Carbon Fields

Grass is a form of solar powered energy – each blade converting sunlight into food for animals that are the next link to us in the food chain. Farmers have used this fundamental way of harnessing the power of the sun in a system that goes back to the time when we moved on from being hunter-gatherers. Grass literally laid the seeds of all human societies across the globe.

In just 50 years in Britain changes in farming practice have disrupted this simple process in which growth generated by the sun sustains all life forms. We now employ industrial methods in farming that make growing food oil-dependent. Chemical production, transport to move chemicals, grains and other fodder crops, treating and harvesting crops with fuel-hungry machines all combine to give modern farming a huge carbon footprint.

Our traditional methods of mixed farming involved grazing stock, maintaining hay meadows and growing cereals and vegetables in a system of crop rotation. The patchwork landscape that had developed after the enclosures of the eighteenth century provided species-rich habitats. These habitats continued to flourish until the 'green revolution' of the 1970s when pastures were ploughed to grow chemically-dependent cereals over much of lowland Britain. The grain mountains of the 80s and 90s generated by subsidies from the EU were used to feed cattle and sheep. Around a half of the cereals grown in Britain are used as animal fodder in today's intensive farming systems.

In eliminating the species-rich pastures and hayfields that were the bedrock of British pastoral agriculture for millennia, we have in effect collapsed an ecosystem that sustained some of the most cherished species of our farmland such as the hare, the skylark, lapwing, curlew, corncrake, snipe and grey partridge.

There is now general alarm at the loss of honey bees but we have neglected to think of the complex web of insect life that sustains our summer visiting birds: swallows, martins and swifts, warblers, chats, flycatchers and many other species. These insects are also responsible for pollination of both wildflowers and crops.

The changes to arable farming are easy to see and understand. The prairie-like cereal fields that cover much of lowland Britain had become wildlife deserts. But so too are many of our grasslands.

Once common butterflies such as the meadow brown, small copper and orange tip have become scarce. These are losses that we can see, but what lies beneath the bright green fields of chemically sustained ryegrass is a collapse of microscopic life forms, the bacteria, fungi, protozoa and nematodes which break down and recycle nutrients from animal dung and maintain the natural fertility of the soil. These life forms are at the bottom of our food chain. Next up are the grubs and worms that not only feed the birds of the fields but also aerate the ground to sustain the fertility and growing power of the soil.

The deep-rooted herbs that used to flourish in the meadows like chicory and dandelion reach into the earth, help to get air and organic matter into the soil and to bring minerals and trace elements up to the surface. Clovers fix nitrogen from the air and build soil fertility naturally, removing any need for carbon-loading nitrate fertiliser.

Plant species that make up diversity in grassland such as plantains, sorrel, birds foot trefoil, vetches, yarrow, bedstraw, knapweed, dandelion, ox-eye daisy, red clover and hay rattle, provide forage for hares. They also have health-giving properties that keep not only hares healthy but also the ruminants that graze there.

Animals kept on traditional pastures are usually healthy and have no need of mineral supplements. They tend not to suffer from the debilitating lameness and infections endemic in the national herd. Cattle are able to self-medicate just as wild animals are, by selecting a nutritious balance of plant foods that have medicinal properties and they pass on the health giving properties of their food in the milk we drink and the meat we eat.

It is known that meat and dairy products from animals fed mainly on grass contain much higher levels of a range of vitamins, omega-3 fatty acids and an important compound CLA (conjugated linoleic acid) which has been shown to protect against cancer, diabetes, heart disease and obesity.[23]

There are many people now who can testify to the great taste of naturally produced meat and dairy products and there is a resurgence of interest in sustainably produced animal products.

'Throughout history grass has been the nation's most important crop, its greatest wealth creator...If all British farmers were to make full use of our great grassland resource we would all benefit. We'd enjoy healthier foods and a diverse, less polluted countryside'[24].

When the natural fertility of the land is lost, it needs a constant, expensive, oil-hungry chemical fix; but we know that the oil is running out. We also know that the continued burning of fossil fuels is causing climate change at a rate that will threaten all life on earth.

In his illuminating and important book, *Carbon Fields - how our countryside can save Britain*, Graham Harvey maintains that if you take oil out of the equation and go back to feeding cattle and sheep all year round on grass (grazing outside for much of the year and feeding hay in winter), the health of the nation could be improved with what comes for free from the grass.

Over and above extolling all these environmental and health benefits, Graham Harvey spells out very clearly the role that farming could play in reducing the greenhouse gas emissions that it currently produces on a massive global scale. But this would require a hands-off approach. In short, it means working by more traditional methods and allowing soils to capture carbon in organic matter instead of releasing it into the atmosphere.

'According to a Royal Society estimate, carbon capture by the world's farmlands could total as much as ten billion tonnes of carbon dioxide a year, given better management of the soil. That's more than the annual carbon dioxide accumulation in the atmosphere. A different form of agriculture – with more emphasis on grassland production – wouldn't merely help with the problem of global warming; it could solve it[25]

Farming in the Derbyshire Dales

Alarm at the rate of loss of many species as the result of several decades of intensive farming triggered the first of a series of agri-environmental schemes in the 1980s aimed at supporting farmers and landowners in managing land to benefit wildlife. The latest of these – Environmental Stewardship is open to all farmers, land managers and tenants in England. The scheme is administered by Natural England on behalf of DEFRA. Farmers are given financial support and advice on how to manage their farms in environmentally sensitive ways. The scheme operates at different levels with Entry level, Organic and Higher level stewardship enabling farmers to develop practical environmental management programmes.

Specific measures are taken to encourage certain species, but it is generally the case that what encourages one species will assist all wildlife. The development of field margins, beetle banks and buffer strips in arable areas encourages insect life (helping both pollination and wild birds) and provides cover and corridors along which small mammals can travel. Similarly, hedgerow and meadow restoration and the reduction of pesticide use provide cover and forage for hares and help farmland and other birds. Restoring bio-diversity works literally all the way up the food chain.

Natural England claim that at the start of 2009 nearly two thirds of England's agricultural land was covered by environmental agreements. Various conservation bodies monitor and assess the success of improvement measures but it may be some years before true recovery can happen and there may be conflicts ahead in differently perceived priorities for land use. The best hope is that farmers, conservationists and the British public can unite in maintaining the pressure to keep rebuilding habitat and repairing the damage of previous decades. One thing is certain, further intensification of production is bound to lead to further losses in biodiversity and none of us can afford that.

In the Derbyshire Dales there are some nationally important wildflower meadows. Conservation of these and restoration of other bio-diverse pastures are priorities for the Peak District National Park Authority, Natural England and the Derbyshire Wildlife Trust. But preservation of precious remnants of land is no substitute for more generally sustainable approaches to land use.

The future for the hare and for all British wildlife life lies in the hands of farmers and ultimately us, the consumers. Many farmers across Britain are passionate about the wildlife on their farms but they cannot run their farms as nature reserves. They work under many pressures and have to make hard choices in order to keep their businesses afloat.

Farmers in the Youlgrave area and Lord Edward Manners who owns the Haddon Estate describe how they balance out the demands of farming productively and conserving the wildlife on their land.

For information on specific measures designed to help brown hares see Appendix 5.

John Ely *Hollow Farm, Youlgrave*

John has a large dairy herd of 100 Holstein cows on the home farm.

We're 100% grass and when we improve a field it'll be down to long-term leys. One of the things we've found is the lapwing and curlew have come back where they have the undisturbed ground. We've got more smaller birds, we see buzzards and we've got a barn owl. The hares are coming back as well. The other night there were five altogether in the bottom field. Twenty years ago that would have been a rare sight. There's a couple of foxes and quite a lot of badgers.

I would say 80% of its down to stewardship, but now lads don't come bird nesting or with their air rifles like they did 25 or 30 years ago. The generation that went around poaching are dying out now. Now people come walking the footpaths. The dog works the ground 30 to 40 yards either side of the path and that ground is sterile for wildlife. The year of foot and mouth when we came to mow our fields in the last week of May, we were forever stopping for nests and normally we don't see any.

There are 97 different species of flora on Hollow Farm and a couple of them are quite rare and only come on the lead rakes. We have got to look after things.

While we use all the nasties of sprays and fertilisers, we try to control it and use things in moderation. Everything is used carefully and that's the key to everything.

The pace has increased tremendously. You haven't got to make many mistakes before you're deeply in the red. Everything is so much more expensive now and more high-powered with more pressure on everything. They've taken a lot of the fun out of farming. We're working on such tight margins. I get 24.01 pence per litre for my milk and I've got all the investment of cows, milking parlour, tanks and all the infrastructure of the farm. We do blame the supermarkets. But we're all as bad as each other in that we go and buy the cheaper product.

I see grass fields as units of energy. The cows convert sunlight and water and the naturally occurring minerals into units of energy. If we had got wildflowers and poorer species grass, they wouldn't convert it as well. With the prices we're on at the moment we couldn't make any progress.

Ours can be quite a lonely solitary existence sat in tractor cabs listening to the radio if you're lucky. They're long days. We're working by 6.00 am and it's usually 6.45 pm when we come in at night. We find it very difficult to have a holiday.

Keith Harrop *New Farm, Alport*

Keith has beef cattle, sheep, pigs and farmyard poultry on the home farm. He also rents land in around 15 other places.

We have entered into some Entry level stewardship schemes. They fit in well because we farm five or six hundred acres in different places. We've got 12 acres with some very intensive silage close to home and some ground that isn't treated at all. You can't put muck or fertiliser on. When we've got beasts the muck's got to go somewhere – what else would we do with it?

There isn't a place for haymaking now. We do a bit of haymaking because we want some little bales for calving boxes. We did six acres of hay last year and we had to get the whole family out and we sweated it out for three hours to get those little bales in. We're watching the weather for five days praying it doesn't rain. If it rains, it goes from being lovely stuff to being all dusty. It isn't safe to feed it to anything when it's like that. The silage is better for the cattle. Hay is just too labour-intensive and too risky. There's no place for it where there's no staff on a farm.

My generation has no idea what it's like to be hungry. Its all very well to say we don't need grass on the fields or cows on the fields, lets grow some flowers – but they won't feed us will they?

Time is the major problem. Everything has to be done in the least possible time you can do it because there's never any staff. If you have got them, you've got a million jobs for them to do. You've either got to rush at everything or find a machine that will do it faster because we're spread over such a big area.

We're having to do the jobs of six men now. I know we've got the machines to do these things. It's a bit the government's fault, wanting more and more and more.

Daykin Shimwell *Youlgrave*

Daykin farms on Youlgrave Moor and rents 70 acres at Over Haddon. He has beef cattle and sheep.

Everything's got to be raced now hasn't it? Cattle have got to be finished at ten or eleven months old. I've got to have it done before my neighbour. They're very competitive people, farmers are.

If there weren't fertilisers about and sprays we'd be a lot better off. Over-production has caused a lot of problems especially with milk. If they got rid of fertilisers the job would sort itself out in time.

My dad was always saying 'You don't want to be spraying this and spraying that'. I don't think he wants the wild flowers ruined. I think you've only got one chance with them.

My family have been here since at least the 1750s and we've had the same piece of ground on the moor since 1797. Its never ever been intensively farmed. It's never had fertiliser or sprays on it. It's never had the flowers killed. It's really ancient meadows, a lot of it. It makes lovely hay. But we mainly make it into dry silage. Its beautiful stuff it is. We don't have trouble with lameness or infertility. It may be to do with the herbs and the cattle have got a real shine to them. You've only got to look in the trough in the morning to see what's left – nothing, they eat it all up.

We've got two barn owls up there now and there are buzzards flying about. I don't think I've ever seen so many hares as these last three years.

Since we ploughed the fields at the back we've got fifteen pairs of lapwings. We don't spray them or fertilise them. We don't go on them at all from September till the end of July. So there's plenty of time for the lapwings to nest and hatch.

I think the life of the farmer is hard. There's a lot of pressure on them. One man now is doing the job of six. On a hundred acre farm they're able to have a hundred cows where before they'd only have fifty.

I've always got enough silage. I can't really have any more cattle or sheep on the ground I've got. I don't really see the advantage to buy fertiliser at £220 a ton to put that on and have more cows and more work. I think I've got enough work to do now. It's a lot nicer to see a hare running around and some wild flower meadows than it is not.

Lord Edward Manners *Haddon Hall*

Lord Edward owns 4,000 acres on the Haddon Estate. Most of the estate is tenanted out but he has recently taken on direct management of the home farm.

We're in the first year of organic conversion. I wanted to have a piece of the estate which we could manage ourselves and I think it's very important to be conscious of the wildlife management and the broader habitat issues. The EU, DEFRA and Natural England are very keen on this sort of farming right now and the whole grant structure for farmers has changed with the advent of the Higher level stewardship scheme which enables landowners like myself to conduct conservation farming.

We're very lucky round here. We don't have particularly intensive farming. Its wonderful land and my tenants are very aware of it.

We stopped the commercial shoot here. So we're not putting down thousands of reared pheasants any more. My head keeper is now responsible for habitat management and encouraging wild game birds.

There are many different species which we're hoping to encourage. The real indicators and the difficult ones are ground nesting birds. We have an awful lot of predators here: foxes, badgers and rats. One of our target species is English partridge. We've got six metre buffer strips either side of hedgerows where we're going to plant bird-friendly flowers and grasses.

We have a great population of hares here. If anything, I've seen an increase in hares over the last few years and I think our farm project will really improve that too.

If you give nature half a chance, it bounces back. It's such a forgiving force. And if you take the pressure off the land a bit and do some positive intervention in the management of the land, then that will have enormous benefits all the way up the food chain.

I'm hoping that not only will it benefit wildlife and the environment but that it will be a commercial success too. If you work with nature, if you just step back a bit and let nature recover then you can reap the benefits too. We bought a small herd of longhorn cattle, which is fantastic beef and very sought after. They are wonderful animals. They are browsers rather than grazers so they are very good for land management and they live outside all year round. So it's small output but very high value output. It's kind of old-fashioned farming, but in a modern way.

Mark Swindell *Millfield Farm, Alport*

Mark has a herd of dairy cows and beef cattle.

I am about the fifth generation here. My family bought it from Haddon Estates in the 1920s. We farm about 250 acres in about three main blocks. We're all grass. Now we hardly plough anything up, but we do try and bulk them up and rejuvenate them with direct drilling. We have semi-improved grassland. Compared to some of the farms round here, we have got some old swards with a lot of diversity in them with a lot of herbs. We're in the Entry Level Stewardship scheme but its made very little difference to us because we've got the old established pastures. We have never been an intensive farm, more extensive. So it fitted in well with us.

On the milk side there's a tremendous difference with the modern grasses. It's like feeding the cows rocket fuel, and the growth and quality far exceeds the older pasture. Once you've done a cut and you've put on fertiliser and it rains, the re-growth is there. With the old tired pastures, you get one cut and a bit of grazing and that's it.

There have always been curlew that come back. We try and find the nest and mark it when we mow. The best thing that ever happened to the wildlife was foot and mouth (which kept the walkers and their dogs off the fields).

We keep being told there is going to be a food shortage. I think if there is a food shortage, the pressure on the land to produce more will be so great, I think wildlife will be a secondary consideration.

It is a hard way of life. When I was a child we had two full-time men here. Now just me and my brother (who works part-time) do all the work, farming twice the acreage.

We've farmed here for generations. You are guardians of the countryside to some extent. I probably think I will be the last generation. I can't see my children farming, because Dad's never had a holiday in 30 years.

The future

Brown hares in the Derbyshire Dales, like all hares that live in pastoral landscapes, struggle to survive. There are fewer of them, they are in poorer condition and have lower survival rates than hares in arable land. It was for this reason that a report, prepared for DEFRA in 2004, suggested that it is pastoral landscapes which 'offer the greatest scope for increasing densities and, hence, it is here that conservation efforts should be focussed'. The author, Dr David Cowan concluded that 'enhancing survival and particularly leveret survival should be a specific target for conservation action'.

Increasing the survival rates for both adults and leverets is crucial for population growth. Currently, annual mortality rates for hares in UK pastoral habitats average at 65%. This is at the top end of the 49-65% average range for Europe as a whole. The lower population levels in UK pasture lands mean that our hares are not significant as a game species and receive less attention by way of active conservation measures than they do in some arable areas.

It seems that habitat management gives hares the greatest chance of making the most of their innate skills in escaping and evading predators. A range of different habitats provides cover, open ground and food all year round. There are encouraging signs that hare densities can increase on farms with stewardship agreements and most of the measures aimed at encouraging species diversity benefit hares.

Much of the landscape of the Dales has become hostile to hares because of silage growing and greater density of grazing stock. Areas that have a range of diverse habitats act as oases. An extension and increase in the number of such areas would go some way to increasing our local hare populations and if such measures were adopted throughout the country we could begin to rebalance the population across different landscapes.

The decline in brown hare numbers should be seen in the context of falling populations throughout Europe, but hares have less legal protection in Britain than in almost any other EU country. Most countries operate a close season and, while this appears to have had little impact on hare numbers in those countries, it does address the animal welfare issue of killing lactating females during the main breeding season when orphaned leverets starve to death.

Meanwhile, the future legal status of the hare in the UK – whether it will be classified and seen as a game animal, pest, quarry or a potentially endangered species – still lies in the balance. This is perhaps, because it is as hard for those who have never seen a hare to comprehend the need to cull them as it is for those who see them all the time to recognise the plea for protected status. The best that we can hope for in the future is a more balanced population of hares throughout Britain. This would, in turn, be a measure of the general health of our countryside.

If we give hares the chance to thrive by taking pressure off the land, then all living creatures would benefit, including us. While there are many conflicts of interest between farming, recreational use and wild life conservation in the Peak District National Park, for many farmers, residents and visitors, the prescence of hares enchances the experience of this wonderful landscape.

Appendix 1
The Irish hare

The Irish hare is a sub-species of the mountain hare. It is the slightly larger the mountain hare. Its coat does not turn white in winter, but, like the mountain hare, it has a completely white tail.

The Irish hare lives only in Ireland and has done so for thirty thousand years, since before the last ice age. It is now one of the rarest mammals in Europe and has suffered a dramatic decline in numbers – down 60% between 2007 and 2009. Modern farming techniques, netting for coursing events, shooting and hunting have pushed the Irish hare to extinction in some areas. Elsewhere populations have become fragmented.

The Irish hare is still classified as quarry species but in 2004 it was granted temporary protection in the North of Ireland under a Special Protection Order (SPO). This order is currently under review.

In the Republic of Ireland hunting and coursing of both the Irish hare and the brown hare continue under licence.

Appendix 2
Diseases of the hare

There are a number of diseases that affect hares, some of which cause only mild problems. The principle causes of death by disease are European Brown Hare Syndrome (EBHS), Yersiniosis (Pseudo-tuberculosis), Pasteurella and Coccidiosis.

EBHS was not diagnosed until 1989 and some deaths that may have been caused by EBHS prior to that time, were blamed on the widespread use of the herbicide paraquat [26]. EBHS is a viral disease that causes liver damage and haemorrhage in the lungs. It leads to rapid death so that a hare that has died from this disease may look perfectly healthy.

This disease can spread through populations of hares and have a major impact on numbers. Survivors can develop immunity, but exposure to the disease will affect younger hares who have no resistence.

Yersiniosis and **Pasteurella** are both bacterial infections. Yersiniosis mainly effects adult hares and causes a rapid death. As with EBHS, animals killed by this disease look healthy.

Pasteurella affects both rabbits and hares and mainly presents as an upper-respiratory tract infection frequently leading to death.

Coccidiosis is a parasitic disease that is present in the gut of most hares. Infection involves a rapid spread of micro-organisms that damage internal organs. It is a particular problem in the autumn when hare populations are highest. Wet weather further aggravates the condition.

Leverets and young hares with undeveloped immunity are more prone to this disease than adults. It is a wasting illness and a hare suffering from it will become emaciated before it dies.

Hares are more vulnerable to disease if they are poorly nourished, subject to stress or their population is too dense. Overcrowding of territory caused by loss of suitable habitat can force too many hares to share too little space.

Appendix 3
Hares and the law

- King Richard II made trapping or snaring by poachers, or keeping greyhounds illegal.

- Henry VIII made it illegal for anyone to track and kill a hare in the snow.

- **The Hares Act 1848** allowed unrestricted and unlicensed killing of hares by those who owned or rented enclosed land.

- In 1880 the **Ground Game Act** extended the freedom to kill hares all year round by those owning or occupying any land. This led to a rapid decline in numbers and less sport for landowners as their tenants took hares for the pot or for additional income. Hare meat was highly prized by the Victorians and could command high prices at market.

- The **Hares Protection Act 1892** made it illegal to sell hare or leveret from March 1st until July 31st, and re-imposed the minimal protection they had on Sundays and Christmas Day. These laws apply today.

- The **Hunting Act 2004** made it illegal to hunt wild animals with dogs and outlawed hare coursing.

Legislation in the past has had far more to do with protecting elite sporting opportunities than concern for the welfare of hares or wildlife conservation.

Appendix 4
Loss of farmland birds

Lapwing

The lapwing or peewit, once a common bird of moors and farmland, has crashed in numbers and the large flocks that were commonplace over 50 years ago have become something of a rarity. From the mid 80s to the mid 90s, 50% of the remaining flower-rich hay meadows of the Peak District were lost. In that same period, numbers of lapwing on the North Staffordshire Moors suffered a decline of 72%[27].

This collapse in lapwing numbers has been succeeded by further decline. A survey conducted by volunteers for the RSPB in 2002[28], revealed around 1200 pairs in the Peak District. In 2007 a repeat survey estimated the population to be between 500 and 600 pairs. While the results have not been fully analysed, this suggests that in just five years the population has suffered a further 50% decline.

Lapwing have been found to be twice as successful in rearing their young on land appropriately managed under environmental stewardship schemes. In these areas, populations could remain stable with a better rate of success in raising chicks to fledging. In areas that are not managed, the lower rate of breeding success points to a population decline at the rate of 8% a year.

Curlew

In the mid 80s to the mid 90s, the curlew suffered a similar pattern of population decline to the lapwing with a 57% decrease in numbers in the North Staffordshire Moors. There were 421 pairs in 1985. In 1996 just 179 pairs were found.

In 1990 the curlew population for the whole of the Peak District was around 2000 pairs, 455 of which were on moorland.

In 2002 the Lapwing and wader survey in the Peak District and surrounding area recorded just 264 pairs of curlews, mostly in farmland. Those on moorland were not surveyed, but it is thought that pairs are likely to be moving from the farmland and in-bye to breed on moorland areas.

Skylark

Nationally, skylark numbers have dropped by 50% since the 1980s, a rate of decline which has made them a 'Red List Bird' of Conservation Concern. As a large proportion of them breed in arable areas, the intensive methods now used are considered responsible. In the 1960s, 80% of cereal crops were sown in spring; now just 20% are sown then. This produces a tall crop of autumn sown cereals which are unsuitable for nesting in late spring, so skylarks raise fewer broods. The loss of winter stubbles means less food then and the intensive management of arable fields, in particular the use of agro-chemicals, reduces both insect and plant foods for skylarks through spring and summer.

Common Snipe

It is not easy to survey this species, but it is thought that the population has suffered from the difficulties faced by other birds of farmland.

Appendix 5
Hare conservation:
Dos and don'ts[29]

Dos

- Hares like a 'patchwork quilt' farmland. Break up large blocks of cereal as much as possible.

- Use set-aside as a wildlife habitat. A series of 20-metre strips is ideal if it is planted under the Wild Bird Cover Option.

- On arable farms, mown grass strips will provide summer grazing. Run them across open fields rather than alongside hedgerows where predators may lie in wait.

- Hares need quiet, undisturbed cover for raising leverets. On livestock farms leave some areas of grass uncut and ungrazed for leverets to hide in.

- When making silage, cut the field from the centre outwards rather than from the outside in, so that hares can escape the machinery into neighbouring fields.

- Planting game crops for pheasants will provide cover and food for hares.

Don'ts

- Don't use herbicides such as paraquat, which are known to kill hares.

- Don't shoot hares in late winter unless you are sure crops are being damaged. A February hare shoot can remove 60% of the breeding stock.

- Don't let poaching jeopardise the hare population. Contact the local police Wildlife Liaison Officer to get help on this.

References

1   Ewart Evans and Thomson, *The Leaping Hare*

2   Tapper and Yalden, *The Brown Hare*

3   Derek Yalden, personal communication

4   Derek Yalden, personal communication

5   Tapper and Yalden, *The Brown Hare*

6   Hutchings and Harris, The current status of the brown hare in Britain

7   Game and Wildlife Conservation Trust, Trends in brown hare numbers

8   Hutchings and Harris, The current status of the brown hare in Britain

9   Carnell, *Hare*

10 Ewart Evans and Thomson, *The Leaping Hare*

11 Tapper and Barnes, Influence of farming practice on the ecology of the brown hare

12 Smith, Jennings, Tataruch, Hacklander and Harris, Vegetation quality and habitat selection by European hares (Lepus europaeus) in a pastoral landscape

13 Barnes, Tapper and Williams, Use of pastures by brown hares

14 Ewart Evans and Thomson, The Leaping Hare

15 Boggan, Gangsters, guns and unlicensed gambling: welcome to the world of illegal coursing, *The Independent* 05.01.2002

16 William Blake, *The Auguries of Innocence*

17 Stoate and Tapper The impact of three hunting methods on brown hare (Lepus europaeus) populations in Britain

18 Lovegrove, *Silent Fields*

19 Cowan, An overview of the current status and protection of the brown hare

20 Hutchings and Harris, *The current status of the brown hare in Britain*

21 Reynolds, Stoate, Brockless, Aebischer, Tapper, The consequence of predator control for brown hares (Lepus europaeus) on UK farmland

22 David Read, Personal communication

23 Harvey, *Carbon Fields*

24 Harvey, *Carbon Fields*

25 Harvey, *Carbon Fields*

26 Edwards, Fletcher and Berny, Review of the factors affecting the decline of the European brown hare

27 Peak District National Park Authority, *A Living Landscape*

28 Sugrue, Lapwing and wader survey 2002: Peak District and surrounding area

29 Conserving the Brown Hare, from a leaflet produced by the Game Conservancy Trust

Bibliography

A Living Landscape – A Biodiversity Action Plan for the Peak District, Peak District National Park Authority, 2001

Ancient and/or species-rich hedgerows action plan, *UK Biodiversity Action Plan*, www.ukbap.org.uk

Barnes, RFW, Tapper,SC, and Williams, J, Use of pastures by brown hares, *Journal of Applied Ecology*, 20, 179 – 185, 1993

Biodiversity loss brings ecological systems closer to a tipping point, UN News Centre, 22 May 2010, www.un.org

Blake, William, Auguries of innocence

Boggan, S Gangsters, guns and unlicensed gambling, *Independent*, 5 January 2002

Brown hare action plan, Cheshire Region Biodiversity Partnership, www.cheshire-biodiversity.org.uk

Brown hare interim distribution map March 2010, Derbyshire Mammal Group, www.derbyshiremammalgroup.com

Brown hare species action plan, *UK Biodiversity Action Plan,* www.ukbap.org.uk

Brown Hare, Species information note, Natural England, May 2007

Calcareous grassland habitat statement, *UK Biodiversity Action Plan*, www.ukbap.org.uk

Campaign for the Farmed Environment website, www.cfe.or.uk

Carnell, Simon, Hare, Reaktion Books, 2010

Clover, Charles, Schemes failing to save wildflower meadows, *Daily Telegraph*, 13 May 2002

Conserving the brown hare, Game Conservancy Trust, 2002

Cowan, David, An overview of the current status and protection of the brown hare (*Lepus Europaeus*) in the UK, report for European Wildlife Division, DEFRA, August 2004

Demand an end to coursing licenses, *Animal Voice, the Newsletter of the Irish Council Against Blood Sports*, 10, 2009

Edwards, PJ, Fletcher MR and Berny, P, Review of the factors affecting the decline of the European brown hare (*Lepus Europaeus*) and the use of wildlife incident data to evaluate the significance of paraquat, *Agriculture, Ecosystems and Environment*, 79, 95 – 103, July 2000

End of the road for hare coursing, 24 January 2005, www.bbc.co.uk,

Ewart Evans, George, and Thompson, David, *The Leaping Hare*, Faber 1972

Gamekeeping and hare numbers, Game and Wildlife Conservation Trust, www.gwct.org.uk

Governments must act swiftly to salvage biodiversity, UN News Centre, 10 May 2010 www.un.org

Guy, Lynn, Illegal hare coursing in Lincolnshire, 7 January 2008, www.bbbc.co.uk,

Hare courser defends illegal sport, 16 October 2009, www.bbc.co.uk

Hare coursing in Barlborough, 24 May 2009, *Derbyshire Times*

Hare Preservation Trust web site, www.hare-preservation-trust.co.uk

Harvey, Graham, *The Carbon Fields*, Grass Roots 2008

Hutchings, MR and Harris, S, The current status of the brown hare (*Lepus Europeaus*) in Britain, Joint Nature Conservation Committee, 1996

Jowitt, Juliette, UN report warns of economic impact of biodiversity loss, 10 May 2010, *The Guardian*

Ki-moon, Ban, The deadline has arrived, *UN Chronicle*, Archive, www.un.org

Look After Your Land with Environmental Stewardship, Natural England, 2009

Lovegrove, Roger, *Silent Fields*, OUP 2007

Mason, Jill, *The Hare*, Merlin Unwin 2005

Minister extends measures to protect Irish hare, Northern Ireland Environment Agency, 10 September 2009, www.ni-environment.gov.uk

Peak District Landscape Strategy 2009 – White Peak, Peak District National Park Authority, July 2009

Pearce, D, Birds Project Officer, Peak District National Park Authority, Populations of breeding lapwing, common snipe, curlew and twite in the Peak District, unpublished, 2009

Rendle, M, The impact of enclosed coursing on Irish hares, Irish Hare Initiative, January 2006, www.irishhare.org

Reynolds, JC, Stoate, C, Brockless, MH, Aebischer, NJ and Tapper, SC, The consequences of predator control for brown hares (*Lepus europaeus*) on UK farmland, *European Journal of Wildlife Research* 56: 541 – 549 (2010)

Rio Declaration on Environment and Development, United Nations Environment Programme, www.unep.org

Skylark case study, RSPB, www.rspb.org.uk

Smith, RK, Jennings, NV, Tataruch, F, Hacklander, K and Harris, S, Vegetation quality and habitat selection, *Acta Theriological* 50 (3), 391 – 404, 2005

Stoate, C and Tapper, SC, The impact of three hunting methods on brown hare (Lepus europaeus) populations in Britain, *Gibier Faune Sauvage*, 10, 229-240

Sugrue, A, Lapwing and Wader Survey 2002, Peak District and surrounding area, RSPB

Taking Action for Biodiversity – The Brown Hare, Derbyshire Wildlife Trust

Tapper, SC and Barnes, RFW, Influence of farming practice on the ecology of the brown hare (*Lepus Europaeus*), *Journal of Applied Ecology*, 23, 39 – 52, 1986

Tapper, Stephen and Yalden, Derek, *The Brown Hare*, The Mammal Society, 2010

Tapper, Stephen, *The Brown Hare*, Shire Natural History 1987

The hare, National Coursing Club, www.nationalcoursingclub.org

The Irish hare, hunting and coursing, Irish Hare Initiative, www.irishhare.org

Trends in brown hare numbers, Game and Conservation Wildlife Trust, www.gwct.org.uk

UK Biodiversity Action Plan, Highlights from the 2005 Reporting Round, DEFRA, 2006

United Kingdom Biodiversity Action Plan, HMSO, 1995 (includes the brown hare species action plan.)

Williams, SB, Payne, RC and Wilson, AM, Functional specialisation of the pelvic limb of the hare (*Lepus europeus*), *Journal of Anatomy*, April 2007, 472 – 490

List of photographs

All photographs ©Christine Gregory

Acknowledgements

I am very grateful to have had the opportunity to work on this project and I wish to thank a number of people for their expertise, time, support and encouragement. I would like to thank Patricia Stubbs for her close reading, editing, and advice on the text from the earliest stages; and to Caroline Firenza for her wonderful design work and patience over the endless reshuffling of pictures and words.

Thanks to Professor Sir David Read who was immensely helpful with his advice on grasslands, assisting me with research papers, and for his comments and suggestions; and Dr Derek Yalden (President of the Mammal Society) for his generosity in reading and commenting on the text and for providing valuable information.

Several officers of the Peak District National Park Authority have furnished me with advice, documents and contacts. I am especially grateful to Richard Godley who supported this project from the outset and gave me advice and guidance on how to set it in motion; Karen Shelley-Jones and David Pearce for reading and commenting on the text and providing me with information and Rebecca Penny for her support in communicating and providing contacts. I would also like to thank Anna Evans and Jane Proctor at the Derbyshire Wildlife Trust.

The landscape that is the subject of this book would not exist without the stewardship of all the local farmers. My thanks go to John Ely, Keith Harrop, Lord Edward Manners, Daykin Shimwell and Mark Swindell who kindly agreed to be interviewed and whose words form a key part of the text. I am also indebted to Andrew and John Bingham who gave me permission to go haring on their land.

Thanks to Eve Shrewsbury for permission to include Dave Sheasby's beautiful poem; to Diana Mead for showing me the mountain hares; and last but not least, to Tony and Lucy Mead for their encouragement, constructive criticism and patience over many disturbances at dawn.

The brown hare in the wet grass
Stood up ears to the sky
Eyes like brown marbles
Waiting for me to make
The next move
And when I did of course
went away like a
Spring had snapped. Somewhere
like he had been summoned
That second by a very much
Higher power and had no choice
Leaving me in tears.

Dave Sheasby

20 September 1940 – 26 February 2010